Unit 5
Growing and Changing

Contents

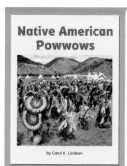

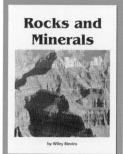

Judge Marge

by Rosa Acosta
illustrated by Deirdre Betteridge

It was the first day of the county fair. Usually, Marge made fudge and pies for the cooking contests. She knitted hats and mittens for the knitting contest. She got lots of prizes every year.

This year Marge had made a pledge.

"I decided I will not enter any contests," she said. "This time I am just going to have fun!"

Marge went into a large room. "Now I can just watch the fudge contest," she said. "I do not have to do a thing!"

A man with a badge rushed up. "Please help us, Marge!" he cried. "We do not have a judge for the contest. You always made the best fudge. I bought lots of it. Will you be the judge?"

"OK," said Marge. "But then I'll relax."

3

Marge tasted so much fudge that her tummy bulged. She gave the first prize to Mrs. Strange.

"Now I will have fun," said Marge.

"Marge, we need you!" cried Mrs. Cage. "We do not have a judge for the pie contest. Will you do it? Your pies were always the best!"

"That's true," said Marge. "I will judge the pies. THEN I will have fun."

Marge tasted half the pies. Her tummy bulged more. She tasted the rest of the pies. Then she gave out the prizes.

"I feel huge," groaned Marge. "I never want to look at a wedge of pie again!"

Marge went into another room. She started to look at hats and mittens. Mrs. Ridge charged up to her. She had on a badge.

"We need you to judge hats and mittens," said Mrs. Ridge.

Before Marge could say a thing, Mrs. Ridge wedged a hat on her head. It was tight and had lots of fringe.

"Do you like it?" asked Mrs. Ridge.

"Help!" said Marge. "I can't judge hats and mittens if I can't see them!"

Marge judged the hats and mittens. Then she sat down near a stage.

"Who makes the best bird sounds?" asked a man. "Marge, will you be the judge?"

A boy chirped. Lots of birds flew to the stage. Birds landed on Marge. They liked her fringe and the bits of pie and fudge.

Marge judged the contest. She gave one boy the prize.

"Being a judge is too hard," said Marge. She leaned against the stage.

Marge made a new pledge. "Next year I will make fudge and pies," she said. "I will knit hats and mittens. That will be fun. And it will be easier than being a judge!"

The Library

by Lisa Shulman

Getting Started

A **library** is a special place. It has a lot of books on each shelf, but it is not a bookstore. The library books are not for sale. We can borrow the library books to read or look through.

People like to use the library. We can use it for free. The library is a good place to read and learn. Let's find out more!

Big, Small, or with Wheels

There are different kinds of libraries. Most towns have a public library. Most schools have a library, too. Some libraries even move around on wheels!

A public library can be big or small. It has books and other things for people to read or look at. A **librarian** helps you check out books to take home.

A school library has books for
children and teachers. It has books
on many different subjects. You can
check out the books to use together
in class or just to read for fun.

This library is in a van called a
bookmobile. The bookmobile brings
books to places that do not have
libraries. It may stop near homes or
at a shopping mall. Who is the driver?
Usually, it's the librarian!

The Library of Congress is our national library. It is in Washington, D.C. This library is huge! In fact, it is the biggest library in the world.

Finding Books and More

A public library has hundreds and hundreds of books. It also has newspapers and magazines. It may have tapes, maps, films, and CDs, too.

Each of these things is kept in its own place. This makes it easy to find what we need. **Card catalogs** or **computers** can help us find things in a library.

Children's books are kept in the children's room. A children's librarian usually works there. Books for adults are in the main part of the library.

The books on fiction shelves are organized by the author's last name. Librarians place these books on the shelves from A to Z. This alphabetical order can help us find the books we want or need.

Most libraries use special numbers or letters to put nonfiction books in order. Books on the same subject have similar numbers.

Let's Use It!

The library's card catalog or computer can help us find books. This is not hard. The librarian can show us how.

We can look up a book's title or the last name of the author. We can also look for a book by its subject. Let's see how this works on the computer.

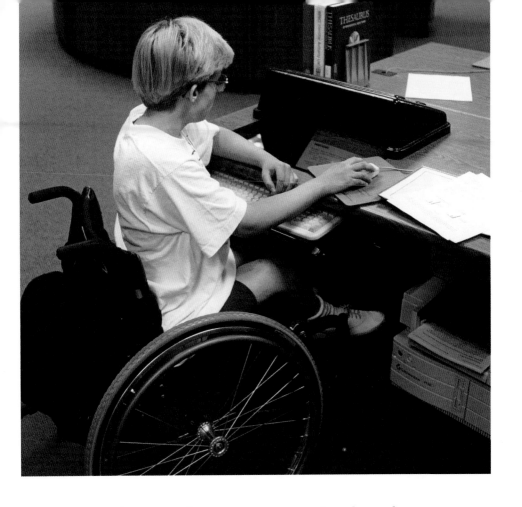

Let's say that you need a book on pandas. Type the word *panda* on the computer. The screen will show a list of books on pandas. A book's number helps you find it on the shelf.

You will need a library card to
check out books. Most public libraries
offer free cards. The librarian can tell
you how to get a card.

Show your card when you check
out books. Take care of the books you
borrow. Remember to return them on
time. These rules help make the library
a place we all can enjoy!

Index

Calvin's Pumpkin

by Sandy Riggs
illustrated by Wednesday Kirwan

Calvin and his mom had planted pumpkin seeds. Now they were looking at rows and rows of pumpkins in the field.

"There must be a hundred pumpkins!" Calvin said.

"Did you hear about the farm fair?" his mom asked. "There will be a pumpkin contest. The biggest pumpkin will win a prize."

Calvin ran out to the field. "I think I can find a big pumpkin for the fair!" he shouted.

"I'm certain you can find a very big pumpkin," Mom said.

It did not take Calvin long to find a big pumpkin. "Look at this pumpkin," Calvin yelled to Mom. "It's huge!"

Mom helped Calvin roll the huge pumpkin to Dad's truck. Dad put the pumpkin in the back of the truck. Then Mom, Dad, and Calvin went to the fair.

At the fair, Dad drove over a big bump. Bang! The back of the truck opened. Calvin's pumpkin rolled out! It broke into two parts.

"Well," said Mom. "Let's try to put the parts together." So they did it. They pressed the parts together and made a whole pumpkin!

Soon a man said, "It has a crack. But it is the biggest pumpkin of all. Calvin wins first prize!" Calvin grinned a very big grin!

After a while, Mom, Dad, and Calvin went home. Dad made a very big pumpkin pie! Everyone ate a sandwich. Then everyone ate a very big slice of pumpkin pie!

Native American Powwows

by Carol K. Lindeen

Getting Started

Does your family or community ever have special **celebrations**? Maybe you have birthday parties in your backyard, or a Fourth of July picnic in the park. Maybe your community has a certain fair or a **festival** in the summer.

Native Americans have a kind of **ceremony** called a **powwow**. They have powwows for many different reasons. A powwow can seem a lot like a picnic, with food and games. Some powwows also include dancing and drumming. People come from all over to take part in these celebrations.

A powwow is a celebration of Native American culture. This means that the powwow is an important part of Native American traditions and beliefs. Keep reading to find out more about powwows.

Dancing

Long ago, Native Americans did special dances before their fighters went to war. They also danced to wish their hunters good luck before the hunt. Other dances also helped to celebrate their return.

Today, Native Americans still gather for powwows. They do these traditional dances to show pride in their culture. Older members of a tribe might teach younger members how to perform the dances. Powwows are usually happy gatherings. People of all ages join in the fun.

Dancers wear traditional Native
American clothing at powwows. Their
outfits are often made of animal
skin, feathers, and colorful beads.
Sometimes dancers pretend to be
animals and act out a hunt or a **legend**.

Many Native American dances are
done to honor certain spirits or gods.
A dance can tell a story or ask a spirit
for help. One person might dance
alone. Men and women can dance in
separate groups or all together.

A rain dance is a special dance to
pray for rain. With their movements,
the dancers ask the gods to send rain
to help the tribe's crops grow. Many
Native American farming tribes do
corn dances for a good harvest.

Music

Music is a big part of Native American celebrations and culture. Dancing and drumming go hand in hand at a powwow. The dancers stomp their feet and move to the beat of the drums. Songs and chants follow the drum **rhythms**.

Groups of drummers usually form a circle at a powwow. The beating of the drums is like the heartbeat of the celebration and of all the people. The drummers play all kinds of songs for the dancers and the crowd.

Drums are the most important
instruments at a powwow. Traditional
Native American drums are made of a
hollow wooden bottom. The top of the
drum, called the head, is made of the
dried skin of a deer, cow, or buffalo.

Native Americans use other instruments at powwows, too. They shake rattles made of wood or gourds. Sometimes dancers attach bells to their clothes or legs. The bells jingle when they dance.

Sometimes singers sing along to
the beat of the drums. The drummers
or dancers can also do the singing.
They often sing words in their tribe's
language. The songs can tell stories or
express feelings.

Food

In the past, Native Americans would celebrate after a big hunt. The whole tribe would **feast** on the meat the hunters brought back. The hunters would tell stories about how brave they were.

The members of some Native American tribes had a corn festival when the corn in the fields was ready to eat. The festival lasted for four days. The people danced and feasted on the new corn. They also drank a special kind of tea called "black drink." Some Native American tribes still have ceremonies like the corn festival to honor their culture.

At today's Native American celebrations, you can find all kinds of food. Corn soup, buffalo burgers, and Indian tacos are a few of the things people eat at powwows.

Fry bread is a tasty treat many
people like to eat at Native American
celebrations. A ball of dough gets
flattened, then fried in hot oil. You
can eat fry bread with your hands.

Today, even if you are not part
of a Native American tribe, you are
welcome at most public powwows.
You can see, hear, and taste Native
American culture at one of these fun
celebrations!

Index

Decode It

by Liane B. Onish
illustrated by Holli Conger

Irene moved her violin case off
the table. Noah, the new boy, sat
down and opened his lunchbox. So
did Irene. Inside, she found a note.

"Who's that from?" asked Noah.

Irene said, "My mom. She writes me notes to remind me of stuff. She often writes them in a secret code."

"You can read that?" he asked.

"Not yet," said Irene. "Today is Friday. So the secret code is plus 5. Let me show you."

Irene wrote the letters *a-z* down the side of a notebook page. Then she wrote numbers under the letters. Irene said, "On Monday, the number 1 stands for the letter *a*. On Tuesday, the second day, 2 stands for *a*. Friday is the fifth day, so 5 stands for *a*."

"I get it," said Noah. "So in Friday's plus 5 code, *a* is 5, *b* is 6, *c* is 7, *d* is 8, *e* is 9, and *f* equals 10."

"That's the idea!" said Irene. "All the way to 30 for *z*."

Irene and Noah decoded the note.
Noah asked, "Who's Yo-yo?"
Irene replied, "My dog."
This is the note from Irene's mom.
Can you decode it?

Rocks and Minerals

by Wiley Blevins

Getting Started

Rocks are all around us. You might find rocks near your home, at the beach, or at the playground.

Some of these rocks may be big enough to sit on. Others may be small enough to hold in your hand.

Did you know that Earth is a huge ball of rock? Earth's rock is broken up into **layers**. The picture on page 55 shows a special view of the inside of Earth. This way, you can see the different layers. Let's take a closer look!

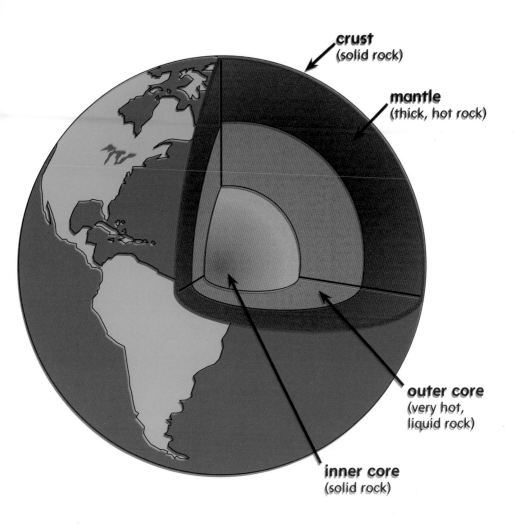

crust
(solid rock)

mantle
(thick, hot rock)

outer core
(very hot,
liquid rock)

inner core
(solid rock)

The top layer is called the *crust*. It is like Earth's skin. It is solid rock. Now look at the other layers. How is the rock different in each layer?

Rocks and Minerals

Not all rocks are the same. Some rocks may be shiny and smooth. Some rocks may have many colors.

Even though rocks may be different, they have something in common. Every rock is made up of minerals. In fact, most rocks are made up of more than one mineral. Rocks are formed by minerals joining together.

There are many different minerals in the earth. People use these minerals in many different ways.

Salt is a mineral. Gold and silver are minerals, too. So are diamonds and rubies. We get salt and other minerals by mining them, or digging them up from under the ground.

Some minerals are made into jewelry.

Kinds of Rocks

There are three kinds, or classes, of rocks. The name of each class tells how the rock was made.

Igneous rocks are the hardest and oldest rocks. The word *igneous* means "fire." Igneous rocks start out as hot, melted rock deep under the ground. This hot, melted rock is called *magma*.

Sometimes magma comes up through cracks in Earth's crust. This may happen when the magma pushes up through an opening in a **volcano**. Magma often comes out as hot **lava**. Then it cools and hardens to form igneous rocks.

Lava flowing from a volcano

Sedimentary rocks are the softest rocks. These rocks are formed from something called *sediment*, or small bits of old rocks.

Water and wind cause rocks to break into small bits. The bits get washed into streams and lakes. Then these bits pile up at the bottom of the stream or lake. Sometimes pieces of shells and sand get mixed in. Over time, the **pressure** of the water pushing down on the rock bits causes them to form into solid rock.

There are many different kinds of sedimentary rocks. Two of these are coal and limestone.

One kind of limestone that students
and teachers may use is chalk. The next
time you use chalk, remember this:
Chalk takes millions of years to form!

Metamorphic rocks are formed in a special way. The word *metamorphic* comes from a very old word that means "to change."

Metamorphic rocks start out as sedimentary rocks or igneous rocks. Then something special happens. The rocks are heated by the earth or squeezed under Earth's crust. This causes the rock to change into another kind of rock. For example, limestone is a sedimentary rock. It is soft. When it is squeezed under Earth's crust, it turns into marble.

A statue made from marble

Marble is a metamorphic rock. Marble is very hard. Builders often use marble as a building material. Besides being very hard, marble can be very beautiful! It is often used to make statues and monuments.

This chart gives examples of rocks and some of the ways these rocks are used.

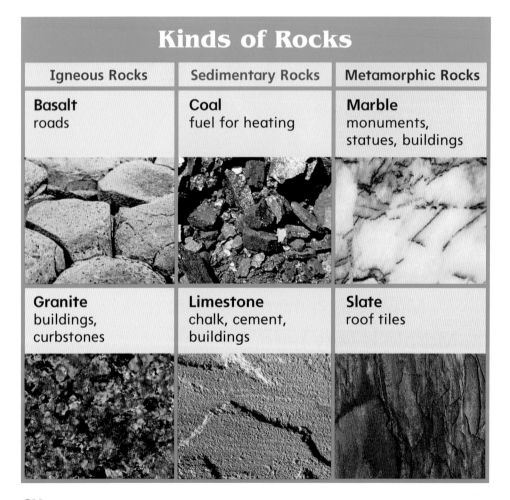

Kinds of Rocks

Igneous Rocks	Sedimentary Rocks	Metamorphic Rocks
Basalt roads	**Coal** fuel for heating	**Marble** monuments, statues, buildings
Granite buildings, curbstones	**Limestone** chalk, cement, buildings	**Slate** roof tiles

Who Studies Rocks?

A rock can "tell a story." Scientists can learn a lot of information by looking closely at a rock. They can learn how the rock was made. They can learn what the rock is made of. They can also learn what Earth was like when the rock was formed.

The scientists who study rocks are called **geologists**. Besides studying rocks, some geologists may choose to study other parts of Earth—soil, mountains, rivers, oceans, and more.

Many other people are interested in rocks, too. Some people like to collect and study rocks as a hobby. These amateur (AM-uh-chur) rock collectors are also known as "rock hounds"!

It's amazing how much rocks can tell us. This rock, like all rocks, has a long and exciting story. Would you and your classmates like to be rock hounds? Would you like to learn what story a rock might tell?

Index

Puddle Pet

By Liz Ray
illustrated by Pete Whitehead

"Look at my new pet," said Jen.
"I found it in a big puddle."

Her friends huddled near Jen's
bowl. A small dark speck swam
over some pebbles.

"It's only a fish," grumbled Jake.
"A fish is nothing special."

"I think this fish is special," Jen told the group. "I'll name him Speckle." She jiggled the bowl and light sparkled off the fish.

"You can't play with a fish or cuddle it," said Jake.

"I like to watch him," said Jen.

Jen took good care of Speckle. She fed him and cleaned his bowl each day. It was fun to watch Speckle swim and blow bubbles.

One day, Jen saw that her fish had little back legs. She was puzzled. Fish don't have legs! What was going on?

Jen kept watching her pet. As Speckle got bigger, his legs got bigger too. Then he grew front legs. His tail became shorter and his body changed shape.

Jen had learned something important. Speckle was not a fish!

"See what Speckle can do now,"
Jen called to her friends.

"A fish can only blow bubbles
and swim," said Jake.

"But Speckle isn't a fish," Jen
said, putting her pet on the table.
"He's a frog, and he can jump!"

Dreaming of Great Ideas

by Judy Giglio

Getting Started

Do you like to take things apart to see how they work? Are you a problem solver? Do you like to dream up new games, puzzles, or toys? If so, you could be an **inventor**!

Think about important things we use each day. We turn on lights. We use vacuum cleaners and dishwashers to clean our homes. Traffic signals tell us when it is safe to walk or drive.

Each of these things is an **invention** that someone made. Many inventions make it easier and safer for people to live.

Around the House

We use some inventions around the house. People used to spend all day cleaning their homes. Today, we have inventions that do a lot of the work for us.

When you turn on a light, thank Thomas Edison. It took him months to invent a lightbulb that would stay lit. Over time, Edison and his crew made more than 1,000 inventions!

Josephine Cochran was tired of washing dishes by hand. She put a wire basket on a wheel in the middle of a copper boiler. Her invention became the first dishwasher!

James Spangler thought of a new way for people to clean dirty floors. In 1907, he made a machine to pick up dirt. The machine had an electric motor. This was the first vacuum cleaner.

During the early 1900s, Clarence Birdseye saw something amazing in the far north. He saw the native people living there freezing fish on the ice. When the fish were later thawed, they tasted fresh! This gave Birdseye a simple idea that led to a great invention—frozen foods!

On the Go

Some inventions help people get from place to place. Today, planes are a fast way to travel. But planes did not always exist.

Two brothers named Wilbur and Orville Wright dreamed of making a flying machine. They built a glider and added a little engine. Their first attempt to fly this glider was in 1903. Even though they had trouble staying in the air, it was an amazing event!

In 1903, Mary Anderson noticed
that car drivers had to stop and get
out to clean their windshields. So
Anderson invented windshield wipers.
Her wipers had a handle drivers used
from inside the car. Now people didn't
need to get out of their cars to clean
their windshields.

In 1923, streets were often crowded with horses, buggies, bicycles, and cars. Garrett Morgan wanted to make streets safer. He made the first traffic signal with the words *Stop*, *Go*, and *Caution*. Traffic signals are an important part of driving safely today.

A **scientist** named Robert Goddard
dreamed of sending rockets to the
moon. His first rocket went only 41 feet
in 1926. But his ideas helped to launch
a spacecraft to the moon in 1969.

Single Minds, *Many* Ideas!

Some inventors had more than one great idea. George Washington Carver was a scientist who worked with plants. He did many **experiments** with peanut plants. His experiments helped him make fruit drinks, oil, soap, flour, milk, ink, glue, paper, and paint—all from peanuts!

Carver found more than 300 ways to use peanuts. He also found more than 100 uses for sweet potatoes.

Chester Greenwood wanted to keep his ears warm in winter. He invented the first pair of earmuffs when he was only 15. Greenwood also invented more than 130 other things. One of his ideas was a teakettle that whistles.

Time Line

Many things we use today were invented a long time ago. You have read about some of them in this book. When were these inventions first created? This **time line** gives you the dates and puts them in order.

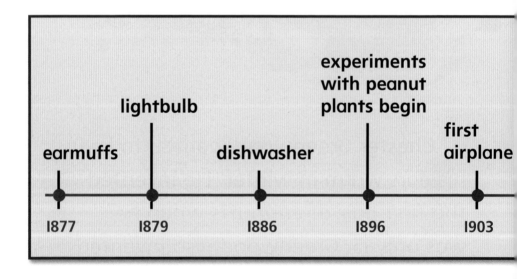

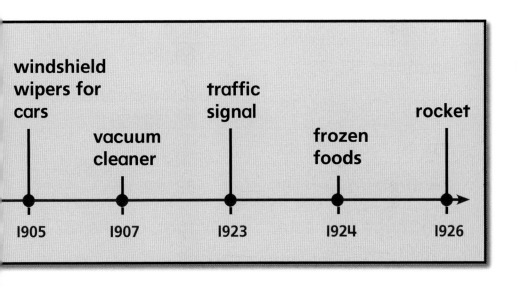

Index

Doggy Door

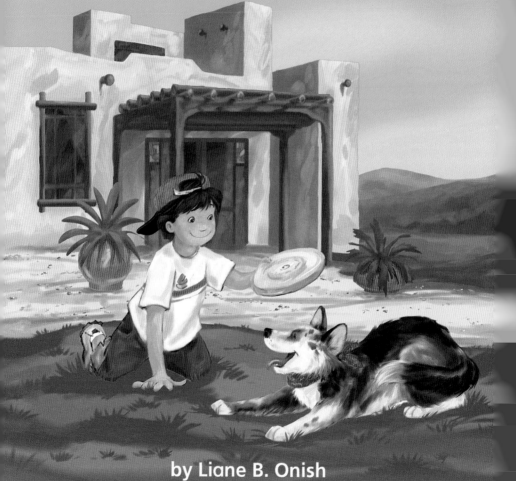

by Liane B. Onish
illustrated by Erin Mauterer

The basement door was open.
Mom said, "Cody, didn't I remind
you to close the basement door
last night?"

"I did remember, Mom. But she
opened it," Cody said.

"Where is she?" Mom asked.

There she was. Sophie, the Irish sheepdog, was sound asleep on the new sofa.

Mom said, "In order to keep the new sofa looking new, Sophie needs to sleep in the basement. How did she get out?"

"Sophie opened the door herself," Cody said.

"I don't believe it! Show me!" Mom said.

So Cody, Mom, and Sophie went into the basement and closed the door.

Sophie stood on the third step and jumped up. Her big front paws hit the doorknob and slid off. Sophie repeated the jumping and pawing until the doorknob turned.

After Cody returned from taking Sophie for a walk, the basement door was open.

"What are you doing, Mom?" he asked.

"I am putting in a new lock!" she said.

Communication Then and Now

by Judy Giglio

Getting Started

How do we tell people what we want? How do they know what we think? How can we help them remember what we mean? We can talk to them. We can show them. We can write down or even draw what we mean.

Whenever we talk, write, or draw, we send a message. We share ideas. This is called **communication**.

How We Communicate

People need to communicate with each other. Communication helps people understand one another better. When we share **information** or news, we can learn new things.

Writing, speaking, and even listening are part of communicating. A person has to listen to a speaker to understand what he or she is saying.

People communicate in other ways, too. When we laugh or cry, we tell how we feel. These people are cheering at a game. Cheering is a kind of communication.

Sometimes people use their hands to communicate. We wave hello or good-bye to a friend. We point to show someone the way. These are all ways to send a message. We do not need to speak.

The First Messages

Very long ago, before we had writing, people found other ways to send messages. They did not use paper. They did not write words.

Drumbeats sent a message from far off. Smoke signals and fires could be seen from far away. These were two ways to send a message. The people who got the message knew how to "read" the sounds or signals.

These pictures were painted a very long time ago. People made these pictures on cave walls to tell a story. What message do the pictures tell about the people who made them?

In the past, ships had signal flags
for sending messages from far away.
Each flag had a special meaning. For
example, one of the flags meant "We
need medical help." As you can see,
signal flags are still used today.

Mail and News

Many letters are sent through the mail today. In the past, this was not easy to do. Mail went by boat or wagon train. It took weeks for news to travel.

People looked for better ways to move mail. In 1860, riders and horses began to carry the mail. This was called the **Pony Express**. The best riders and fastest horses were chosen for the job.

Then came the railroad—and the
mail began to move even faster!
Today, the U.S. Postal Service moves
mail by planes, trucks, and cars. How
does mail reach your home?

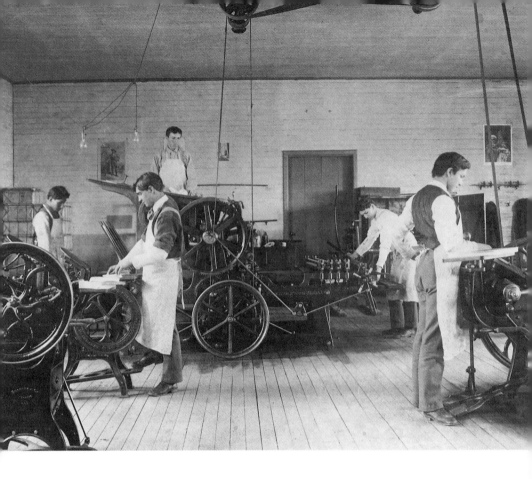

In the past, people looked for
better ways to share news. News
reached more people when the
printing press was used. Many people
could read news items and ads printed
in newspapers or on posters.

Sending Messages Today

Sharing news or information soon became even easier and faster. People began to send messages by voice with the first telephone. Their calls went through telephone wires.

Then came the radio. Sometimes people would get together to listen to news or music on the radio. Then there was television. Besides sound, it had pictures!

These days, information travels
even faster and farther! People are
able to walk and talk at the same
time with a cell phone. Fax machines
send written messages and pictures
through the phone lines.

People use computers in homes, in schools, and at work. **Email** speeds messages to places around the world in a few moments.

What new and faster way to communicate do you think will come next?

Index

Unit 5: Growing and Changing

Week 1: Judge Marge
page 1

to use with *The Tiny Seed*
WORD COUNT: 398

DECODABLE WORDS

Target Phonics Element
closed syllables
> contest, contests, knitted, knitting, mittens, never, relax, tummy

HIGH-FREQUENCY WORDS
> **Review:** again, always, any, bought, decided, do, have, head, into, of, one, said, they, to, want, was, were, who, year

Week 1: The Library
page 9

to use with *The Tiny Seed*
WORD COUNT: 518

DECODABLE WORDS

Target Phonics Element
closed syllables
> biggest, catalogs, children, Congress, different, fiction, hundreds, magazines, nonfiction, number, panda, pandas, public, remember, shopping, similar, subject, subjects

HIGH-FREQUENCY WORDS
> through, together
> **Review:** also, are, have, move, own, people, special, world

CONTENT WORDS
> alphabetical, bookmobile, librarian, library

Week 2: Calvin's Pumpkin *page 25*

to use with *The Ugly Vegetables* **WORD COUNT: 237**

DECODABLE WORDS
Target Phonics Element
closed syllables
biggest, Calvin, contest, grinned, hundred, planted, pumpkin, pumpkins, sandwich

HIGH-FREQUENCY WORDS
certain, field, hundred
Review: into, said, they, to, together, were

Week 2: Native American Powwows *page 31*

to use with *The Ugly Vegetables* **WORD COUNT: 683**

DECODABLE WORDS
Target Phonics Element
closed syllables
attach, bottom, culture, drummers, drumming, express, flattened, happy, harvest, hollow, hunters, members, outfits, picnic, powwow, public, welcome

HIGH-FREQUENCY WORDS
certain, field, hundred
Review: are, brought, have, special, different, people, together

CONTENT WORDS
celebrations, ceremony, festival, language, rhythms, traditional

Week 3: Decode It

to use with *Meet the Super Croc*   **WORD COUNT: 170**

DECODABLE WORDS

Target Phonics Element
   open syllables
      decode, decoded, Friday, Irene, Noah, opened, remind, secret, violin

HIGH-FREQUENCY WORDS
   idea, often, second
   Review: inside, from, of, to

Week 3: Rocks and Minerals

to use with *Meet the Super Croc*   **WORD COUNT: 724**

DECODABLE WORDS

Target Phonics Element
   open syllables
      basalt, broken, even, mining, oceans, opening, over, rubies, shiny, students, volcano

HIGH-FREQUENCY WORDS
   often
   Review: around, building, comes, different, enough, from, into, learn, many, of, other, people, picture, scientists, special, though, together, two, word

CONTENT WORDS
   geologists, igneous, lava, metamorphic, pressure, sedimentary

Week 4: Puddle Pet

to use with *Farfallina and Marcel* **WORD COUNT: 207**

DECODABLE WORDS

Target Phonics Element

consonant + *le* syllables

bubbles, cuddle, grumbled, huddles, jiggled, little, pebbles, puddle, puzzled, sparkled, Speckle, table

HIGH-FREQUENCY WORDS

group, important, only

Review: friends, have, learned, nothing, said, special, was, what

Week 4: Dreaming of Great Ideas
page 75

to use with *Farfallina and Marcel* **WORD COUNT: 606**

DECODABLE WORDS

Target Phonics Element

consonant + *le* syllables

bicycles, handle, little, middle, puzzles, simple, single, teakettle, trouble

HIGH-FREQUENCY WORDS

important

Review: about, always, are, around, do, idea, many, months, of, often, people, scientist, some, their, they, though, to, today, two, were, work

CONTENT WORDS

experiments, invention, inventions

Week 5: Doggy Door *page 91*

to use with *Nutik, the Wolf Pup*   **WORD COUNT: 158**

DECODABLE WORDS
Target Phonics Element
open syllables
asleep, Cody, Irish, open, opened, remind, repeated, returned, sofa

HIGH-FREQUENCY WORDS
door, order, remember
Review: are, putting, said, was

Week 5: Communication Then and Now *page 97*

to use with *Nutik, the Wolf Pup*   **WORD COUNT: 579**

DECODABLE WORDS
Target Phonics Element
open syllables
chosen, email, even, items, moments, music, paper, pony, Postal, posters, radio, riders, saying, writing

HIGH-FREQUENCY WORDS
remember
Review: another, away, carry, does, friend, ideas, laugh, many, move, other, people, pictures, special, talk, they, through, today, together, want, what, words

CONTENT WORDS
communication, information, message

HIGH-FREQUENCY WORDS TAUGHT TO DATE

Grade K	Grade 1				Grade 2	
a	about	down	many	so	above	inside
and	across	early	minutes	some	against	island
are	after	eat	more	soon	America	machine
can	again	eight	mother	sound	among	material
do	against	enough	move	straight	another	morning
for	air	every	never	sure	because	move
go	all	eyes	new	their	began	near
has	along	fall	no	then	behind	number
have	also	father	not	there	believe	off
he	always	find	nothing	they	below	often
here	another	four	now	thought	blue	once
I	any	friends	of	three	body	only
is	around	from	old	through	bought	order
like	away	full	once	today	building	other
little	ball	funny	one	together	built	own
look	be	girl	only	too	carry	paper
me	because	give	open	two	certain	picture
my	been	goes	or	under	city	pretty
play	before	gone	orange	until	color	region
said	begin	good	other	up	country	remember
see	below	great	our	upon	decided	scientist
she	better	grew	out	use	different	second
the	blue	head	over	very	door	song
this	boy	help	people	walked	English	special
to	brought	her	place	want	even	study
was	build	house	poor	warm	family	system
we	buy	how	pretty	water	field	talk
what	by	instead	pull	way	follow	though
where	call	into	put	were	food	through
with	carry	it	ride	who	four	together
you	certain	jump	run	why	group	word
	change	knew	saw	work	happened	world
	climbed	know	says	would	hear	year
	come	laugh	school	write	heavy	young
	could	learn	searching	yellow	hundred	
	does	live	should	your	idea	
	done	love	shout		important	
		make	show			

DECODING SKILLS TAUGHT TO DATE

CVC letter patterns; short *a*; consonants *b, c, ck, f, g, h, k, l, m, n, p, r, s, t, v*; inflectional ending *-s* (plurals, verbs); short *i*; consonants *d, j, qu, w, x, y, z*; double final consonants; *l* blends; possessives with *'s*; end blends; short *o*; inflectional ending *-ed*; short *e*; contractions with *n't*; *s* blends; *r* blends; inflectional ending *-ing*; short *u*; contractions with *'s*; digraphs *sh, th*; compound words; long *a (a_e)*, inflectional ending *-ed* (drop final e); long *i (i_e)*; soft *c, g, -dge*; digraphs *ch, -tch, wh-*; inflectional ending *-es* (no change to base word); long *e (e_e)*, long *o (o_e)*, long *u (u_e)*; silent letters *gn, kn, wr*; 3-letter blends *scr-, spl-, spr-, str-*; inflectional endings *-ed, -ing* (double final consonant); long *a (ai, ay)*; inflectional endings *-er, -est*; long *e (e, ea, ee)*; *e* at the end of long *e* words; long *o (o, oa, oe, ow)*; 2-syllable words; long *i (i, ie, igh, y)*; 2-syllable inflectional endings (changing *y* to *ie*); long *e (ey, y)*; inflectional ending *-ed* (verbs; change *y* to *i*); *r*-controlled vowel /ûr/er, ir, ur; inflectional endings *-er, -est* (drop final e); *r*-controlled vowel /är/ar; abbreviations Mr., Mrs., Dr.; *r*-controlled vowel /ôr/or, oar, ore; compound words; diphthong /ou/ou, ow; final *e* (mouse, house); diphthong /oi/oi, oy; prefixes *re-, un-*; variant vowels /ủ /oo, /ü/oo, ew, ue, u_e; possessives; variant vowel /ô/a, au, aw; singular and plural possessive pronouns; 2-syllable words; *r*-controlled vowel /âr/air, are, ear; contractions; short *a, e, i, o, u*; consonant blends *dr, sl, sk, sp, st*; consonant digraphs *ch,-tch, sh, th, wh, ph*; long *a (a_e)*, *i (i_e)*, *o (o_e)*, *u (u_e)*; soft *c* and *g*; long *a (a, ai, ay, ea, ei)*; consonant blends *scr, spr, str*; long *e (e, ea, ee, ey, ie, y)*; prefixes *re-, un-, dis-*; long *i (i, ie, igh, y)*; compound words; long *o (o, oa, oe, ow)*; inflectional endings *-s, -es*; long *u (ew, u, ue, u_e)*; inflectional ending *-ing*, *r*-controlled vowels er, ir, ur, ear, eer, ere, ar, or, oar, ore, air, are; inflectional endings *-er, est*; silent letters *gn, kn, wr, mb*; diphthong *ou, ow*; diphthong *oi, oy*; variant vowel *oo, ui, ew, ue, u, ou, oe*; variant vowel *oo, ou*; variant vowel *au, aw*; suffixes *-ful, -less*; inflectional ending *-ed*; closed syllables, open syllables, consonant + *le* syllables